Black boy, Fly!

Written by Amanda Lynch
Illustrated by Bonnie Lemaire

© 2021 Amanda Lynch
ISBN 978-1-7345026-4-0
LCCN 2021900682

This book is dedicated to Delores Lynch and Mark Lynch, Jr.
Thank you for raising strong men. Iron sharpens iron.

To my son, Amani,
you are my moon and stars and my sweet face baby.
This is my love letter to you.

Love,
Ma

You are **WORTHY**

Sankofa, joy,
and jubilee.

The living water of your ancestors' faith,
You are amazing grace.

The heartbeat of the diaspora,

Reclaiming once occupied space.

Be encouraged by the words
of Malcolm X,

"Tomorrow belongs to those
who prepare for it today."

AMERICA,

too, is your birthright
and your birthplace.

Black boy, fly!

YOU are FREE

Play the drums: kpanlogo, ashiko, djembe.

Move to the rhythm
of the beat,
step, and sway.

You are a sweet melody
Over a smooth beat.

You are fire and water.

Black boy, fly!

You are a king.

From the margins to the center,
Igniting long-deferred dreams.

You are the soul of our community.
You are everything.

You are the bird
of the sun
and the roots of the
baobab tree.

Black boy, fly!

You can be anything you want to be.

Black boy, fly!

Fly on!

Remember Who You Are

1. You are brave.

2. You are strong.

3. You are more than enough.

4. You are proud.

5. You are kind.

6. You are hard-working.

7. You are honest.

8. You are thankful.

9. You are silly.

10. You are in control of your feelings.

11. You are smart.

12. You are helpful.

13. You are a good friend.

14. You are curious.

15. You are resilient.

16. You are talented.

17. You are a great problem solver.

18. You are a winner.

19. You are joyous.

20. You are peaceful.

21. You are safe.

22. You are healthy.

23. You are confident.

24. You are worthy.

25. You are a star.

26. You are deserving.

27. You are trustworthy.

28. You are amazing.

29. You are consistent.

30. You are capable.

31. You are a leader.

32. You are a dream-maker.

33. You are open-minded.

34. You are your own superhero.

35. You are free to
make your own choices.

36. You are perfect
just the way you are.

37. You are complete.

38. You are your ancestors'
wildest dreams.

39. You are quick-witted.

40. You are assertive.

41. You are a thinker.

42. You are true to yourself.

43. You are deserving.

44. You are a giver.
45. You are loved.

46. You are mindful.
47. You are grateful.
48. You are bliss.
49. You are an advocate
for others.
50. You are generous.
51. You are thoughtful.
52. You are insightful.
53. You are extraordinary.

54. You are remarkable.

55. You are unique.

56. You are valued.

57. You are creative.

58. You are authentic.

59. You are happy.

60. You are gifted.

61. You are determined.

62. You are true to yourself.

63. You are able.

64. You are balanced.

65. You are compassionate.

66. You are magical.

67. You are worth it.

68. You are content.

69. You are comfortable.

70. You are free.

71. You are okay.

72. You are here.

73. You are wise.

74. You are adventurous.

75. You are in charge of how you feel today.
Choose happiness.

76. You are calm.

77. You are an activist.

78. You are able to choose
your own path.

79. You are present.

80. You are successful.

81. You are reliable.

82. You are a good student.

83. You are responsible.

84. You are caring.

85. You are powerful.

86. You are passionate about your goals.

87. You are a changemaker.

88. You are a doer.

89. You are adventurous.

90. You are able to work through difficult times.

91. You are able to manage "big feelings."

92. You are understanding.

93. You are contemplative.

94. You are energetic.

95. You are a young king.

96. You are deserving of good things.

97. You are able to ask for help.

98. You are special.

99. You are courageous.

100. You are a visionary.

Definitions

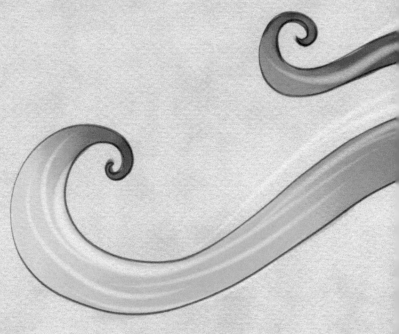

Sankofa (sahn-koh-fah):

In Ghana, the Sankofa is a mythical bird that flies forward while looking backward and holding an egg in its mouth. Translated, it means "go back to the past and bring back what is useful."

Diaspora (dai-a-sp-ruh):

The involuntary mass disbursement of an ethnic or religious group from its native land.

Kpanlogo (pahn-loh-goh):

A type of drum and music that originated in Ghana.

Ashiko (ah-shi-koh):

An Afro-Cuban drum that can be traced to Yoruba
culture in Benin and Ghana.

Djembe (jem-bei):

A type of drum that originated in Mali. It is commonly played throughout West Africa.

Baobab (baw-bab):

A tree that grows in Africa, the Middle East, and Australia. It is commonly referred to as the "tree of life" because it can be used for shelter, food, and medicinal purposes. It has a massive and very resilient root system and is sometimes referred to as "the upside down tree."

Made in the USA
Monee, IL
09 December 2021

84301974R00031